A Friend Is Love

A Friend
Is Love

Adapted by Lynne Suesse

Cover illustrated by Judith Pfeiffer, Linda Prater

Interior illustrated by
Judith Pfeiffer, Tish Tenud, Anne O'Connor,
Linda Howard, Christina Ong

Publications International, Ltd.

Thank you for my friend next door,
And my friend across the street,
And please help me to be a friend
To everyone I meet.

Friends are a little piece of
heaven on earth, a treasure
you can take with you everywhere.

Lord Jesus Christ,
Teach me the ways of friendship
so that I may be a good friend
to someone who needs me,
just like You.

Amen.

A friend loves at all times.
Proverbs 17:17a

Dear Jesus,
Thank you for my friend.
I know my friend is here
to comfort me when
You can't be here Yourself.

Dear friends,
since God so loved us,
we also ought to
love one another.

1 John 4:11

My friend is special to me.
Lord Jesus, please help me
to keep her in my heart
until we grow old.

The guardian angels of life sometimes fly so high as to be beyond our sight, but they are always looking down upon us.

Jean Paul Richter

Lord Jesus,
Help me never to judge another
until I have walked many miles
in her shoes.

Friendship always shines
   On a cloudy day,
Sending rainbows
   To guide your way.
Bright colors of joy
   Painted with love,
A friend is a blessing
   From above.

A friend is like an angel who has earned its wings but still chooses to stay on earth just to be near you, guiding you in your ways and blessing your days.